# Literacy Lifters

## Book 1

Written by Dr. Sheila Twine

Published by World Teachers Press®

Published with the permission of R.I.C. Publications Pty. Ltd.

Copyright © 1999 by Didax, Inc., Rowley, MA 01969. All rights reserved.

First published by R.I.C. Publications Pty. Ltd., Perth, Western Australia.

Limited reproduction permission: The publisher grants permission to individual teachers who have purchased this book to reproduce the blackline masters as needed for use with their own students. Reproduction for an entire school or school district or for commercial use is prohibited.

Printed in the United States of America.

Order Number 2-5082
ISBN 1-58324-004-7

C D E F G H 08 07 06 05 04

Educational Resources

395 Main Street
Rowley, MA 01969

# Foreword

*Literacy Lifters* is a series of books containing practical techniques for working with children who experience difficulties with reading and spelling. All the pages in *Literacy Lifters* have been tried and tested in the classroom. Topics are of high interest to the various age groups of the students, while the skill level has been reduced to suit their needs. Teacher information pages have been included to demonstrate how to use the books to their greatest advantage.

In *Literacy Lifters,* the books do not correspond with any predetermined class grading system. Book One is intended for students at the beginning stages of reading who have not achieved the basic skills. The topics within this book have been written for younger elementary students. Book Two has topics that appeal to middle elementary students and Books Three and Four will appeal to students in middle school and high school. The essence of this series is that it provides high interest content to readers who have not achieved the basic skills of reading and provides for a high level of success within this structure.

I hope you and your students enjoy working through these pages. I certainly enjoyed writing them and became fascinated with the various topics.

## *About the Author*

Dr. Sheila Twine is an educational consultant who has worked with parents, teachers, and students with a variety of abilities in England, Scotland and Australia. She is the author of three books containing practical techniques for working with children who experience difficulties with reading and spelling. She holds a Masters Degree and a Doctorate in Education.

Dr. Twine has been president of various associations and foundations involved with underachieving children with a variety of disabilities from mild intellectual handicap to attention deficit disorder. She was principal of a residential remedial primary school and has been the director of an education consultancy for many years.

The *Topic Pages* for *Literacy Lifters* were tested during the past three years in her consultancy clinics with materials being refined to be of maximum benefit to students with literacy deficiencies.

# Contents

# Program Overview

| Page | Theme and Topic | Phonics | Sight Words | Activity |
|------|-----------------|---------|-------------|----------|
| **Trees** | | | | |
| 10 | Fig Tree | b**ig**, **s**ee | you, this, is | Read and draw |
| 11 | Nut Tree | n**ut**, c**an** | have, make | Read and draw |
| 12 | Gum Tree | g**um**, h**ot** | has, join, Aus/tra/li/a | Join the dots |
| 13 | Evergreen Tree | tr**ee**, d**ot** | ever/green, make | Make a tree |
| **Bugs** | | | | |
| 14 | Bugs | **bu**g, l**eg** | eat, they, leaf | Read and draw |
| 15 | Fly | fl**y**, w**ing** | drag/on/fly | Read and draw |
| 16 | Grasshopper | f**ar**, s**ong** | very | Read and draw |
| 17 | Bats | h**ang**, b**y** | their, an/i/mals | Read and draw |
| **Pets** | | | | |
| 18 | Pup | p**up**, wi**th** | called, tow/el | Read and draw |
| 19 | Vet | v**et**, t**oo**k | said | Read and draw |
| 20 | Fox and Ox | f**ox**, **g**o | what, next, away | Read and draw |
| 21 | Hermit Crab | **cr**ab, Bi**ll** | her/mit, live | Read and draw |
| **Collecting** | | | | |
| 22 | Rocks | ro**ck**, si**x** | lucky | Read and draw |
| 23 | Cards | c**ar**d, c**all** | coll/ect, some | Read and draw |
| 24 | Popsticks | **st**ick, mu**st** | make | Read and draw |
| 25 | Stamps | sta**mp**, b**oo**k | some, come, Can/a/da | Read and draw |
| **Coming Down** | | | | |
| 26 | Cliff | cli**ff**, wi**sh** | rope, steep, cliff | Read and draw |
| 27 | Ski Jump | ju**mp**, c**old** | ski | Read and draw |
| 28 | Rain | r**ai**n, **wh**at | day | Read and draw |
| 29 | Parachutes | d**ay**, **wh**en | par/a/chute | Read and draw |
| **Going Up** | | | | |
| 30 | Rocket | go**ing**, ro**ck**et | fast | Read and draw |
| 31 | Jet | l**and**, l**and**ing | wheel | Read and draw |
| 32 | Balloons | sk**y**, go**ing** | they | Read and draw |
| 33 | Stairs | st**ai**r, hu**ff** | very | Read and draw |
| **Magic** | | | | |
| 34 | Spell | s**p**e**ll**, n**ee**d | magic, sev/en | Read, draw and write |
| 35 | Wizard | sill**y**, wiz**ard** | | Read and draw |
| 36 | Magic Carpet | aw**ay**, **g**o | our, car/pet | Read and draw |
| 37 | Card Trick | pi**ck**, c**ard** | you | Read and draw |
| **Cats** | | | | |
| 38 | Kitten | luck**y**, mess**y** | kit/ten, they, grey | Read and draw |
| 39 | Cheetah | fast**er**, fast**est** | cheetah | Read and draw |
| 40 | Tiger | w**e**, s**oo**n | tiger, hab/i/tat | Read and draw |
| 41 | Circus | su**ch**, **dr**um | circus | Read and draw |
| **Colors** | | | | |
| 42 | Bill | **bl**ack, bu**mp** | | Read and draw |
| 43 | Parrot | **gr**een, t**ell** | par/rot | Read and draw |
| 44 | Willy | sill**y**, **wh**ich | gives | Read and draw |
| 45 | Ice rink | p**ink**, mu**ch** | her, ice rink, mother | Read and draw |
| **Garden** | | | | |
| 46 | Plan | **th**is, wi**th** | | Read and draw |
| 47 | Plants | **pl**an, plan**s** | | Read and draw |
| 48 | Jobs | ha**ve**, plant**ing** | | Read and draw |

© World Teachers Press® – www.worldteacherspress.com

# Teacher Information

## GENERAL LAYOUT

*Literacy Lifters* has been designed to assist students who are experiencing difficulties with reading and spelling. The *Topic Pages* are arranged in groups of themes (building, flying, etc.). There is a Backing Sheet (page 8) which can be copied on the back of each *Topic Page* to provide students with extra space for practice activities. There is also a Word Study Sheet (page 9) provided which shows students some of the anomalies of our language.

## TOPIC PAGES

The *Topic Pages* have been compiled as teaching tools for you and learning activities for students. *Topic Pages* are designed in a special way with a variety of teaching sections.

### Word Study

Research has shown us what students require to become effective readers. Therefore, the *Topic Pages* provide sections for phonically regular, patterned words (found, round, sound), and sight words (the, said, mother) which should be recognized instantly. Studies also demonstrate that efficient readers break up long, unfamiliar words into "chunks" of letters which don't necessarily conform to regular syllables (noct-urn-al, noc-tur-nal) so the *Topic Pages* provide practice in these.

### Comprehension Topic

*Topic Pages* give a variety of activities to promote different types of comprehension. For instance, students need to grasp the main idea of text. Choosing or creating a title assists with this and is featured on every *Topic Page*. The text on each *Topic Page* has blank spaces for students to fill in. This encourages young readers to think and predict as they read so that sensible words can be inserted in the spaces, using clues from meaning and letters provided. Other comprehension activities include literal activities (where the answer is clear from the text), and inferential activities (where students have to think to form sensible answers). For example, "He put on his rain coat. What was the weather like?" Some pages feature following directions and some ask students to make judgements "Would the puzzle have been easier or harder if the shapes had been the same color? Why?"

### Additional Information

At the foot of every *Topic Page* there is a section in smaller print which is at a higher reading level. This is provided to challenge more able students in your group, or could be read by you. It provides additional information on the topic.

## TEACHING TIPS

Two teaching strategies which you may find helpful concerning pre-reading and filling in the blanks:

**1.** Pre-reading is used before students do any reading of the text and is employed to discover what students already know of the topic. For instance, you may say, "Look at the pictures. Now turn the page over and tell me what its about." Your students would then give snippets of information. "It's about snakes." "Some snakes bite and put nasty poison in you." "I felt a snake at the zoo and they are dry." Once students are tuned onto the topic, reading becomes easier, comprehension is better and recall improves. "Three great reasons for spending a few moments before any reading takes place."

**2.** As the *Topic Pages* are teaching tools for you, it is a good idea for your students not to fill in the blanks while you are teaching and going through the various sections with them. The "pencils down" rule allows their whole attention to be focused on what you are saying. Later, comes the practice and activity of filling in the blanks which re-inforces their learning. The Backing Sheet can be used while you are teaching. "Let's spell that word together. Now spell it silently to yourself. Turn your paper over and see if you can write it down." The Backing Sheet has sections for longer words, sight words and phonically regular patterned words.

# Teacher Information

## Topic Pages

The *Topic Pages* have been designed for students who are experiencing difficulties with literacy. They are all pitched to create a high level of interest which will appeal to students with low skill levels.

The *Topic Pages* have been tested in small remedial groups using an ACTIVE teaching mode which is outlined in the model below. Students were encouraged to fill in "gaps" in the *Topic Pages* only *after* teaching had taken place. The Backing Sheet was used *during* the teaching for students to write patterned, chunked and sight words from memory. Topics are arranged in themes and each page contains scope for your active teaching as follows:

### Pre-reading

- Discovering pre-existing knowledge through discussion, with students volunteering snippets of information.

### Comprehension

- Predicting.

- Main idea—creating or choosing titles.

- Cloze activity—to promote thinking and to reinforce word study items.

### Activities

- A mixture of read and draw and phonic activities.

### Incentive

- Children can color the star if they are able to read the additional information. Five stars could equal a reward.

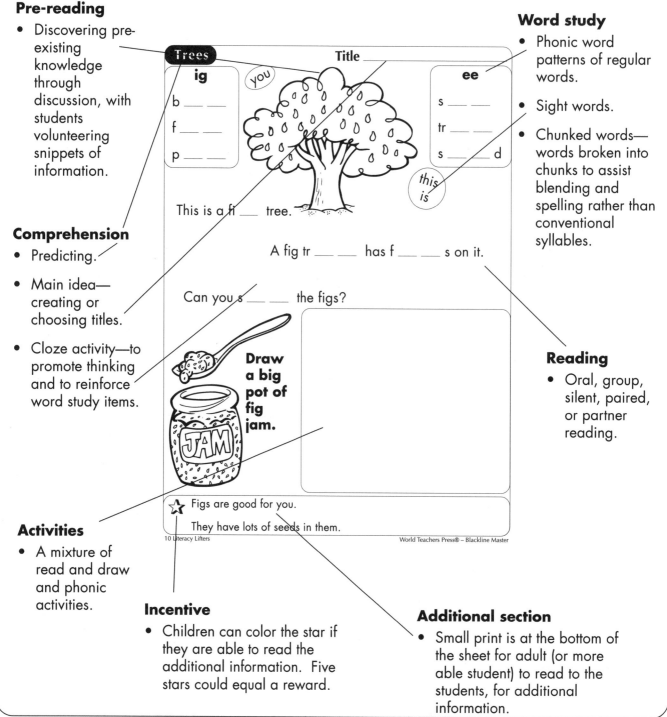

Trees

Title

**ig**
b _ _ _
f _ _ _
p _ _ _

you

**ee**
s _ _ _
tr _ _ _
s _ _ _ d

this is

This is a fi _ _ tree.

A fig tr _ _ _ has f _ _ _ s on it.

Can you s _ _ _ the figs?

Draw a big pot of fig jam.

JAM

☆ Figs are good for you.

They have lots of seeds in them.

10 Literacy Lifters

World Teachers Press® – Blackline Master

### Word study

- Phonic word patterns of regular words.

- Sight words.

- Chunked words—words broken into chunks to assist blending and spelling rather than conventional syllables.

### Reading

- Oral, group, silent, paired, or partner reading.

### Additional section

- Small print is at the bottom of the sheet for adult (or more able student) to read to the students, for additional information.

© World Teachers Press® – www.worldteacherspress.com

# Teacher Information

## Backing Sheet

The Backing Sheet is provided for you to copy on the back of any or all topic sheets. It is general and is designed to complement your teaching. It contains space for further activities in:

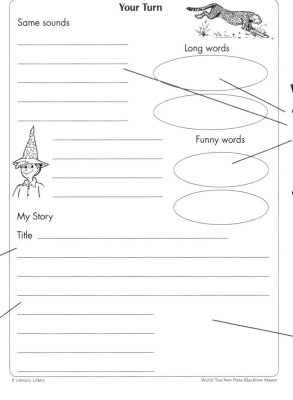

### Writing

- Using titles to describe main idea.

- Single paragraph for younger students.

### Word study

- Patterned words—"Get them in your brain and write them on the back."

- Longer, chunked words or sight words.

### Creativity

- Space provided for students to show understanding with artwork.

## Word Study Sheet

This collection covers many of the oddities which were used in the *Topic Pages*. Hopefully it will show discouraged children one of the reasons they are having difficulties.

# Your Turn

## Same sounds

_____

_____

_____

_____

## Long words

## Funny words

_____

_____

_____

_____

## My Story

Title _____

_____

_____

_____

_____

_____

© World Teachers Press® – www.worldteacherspress.com

# Funny Words

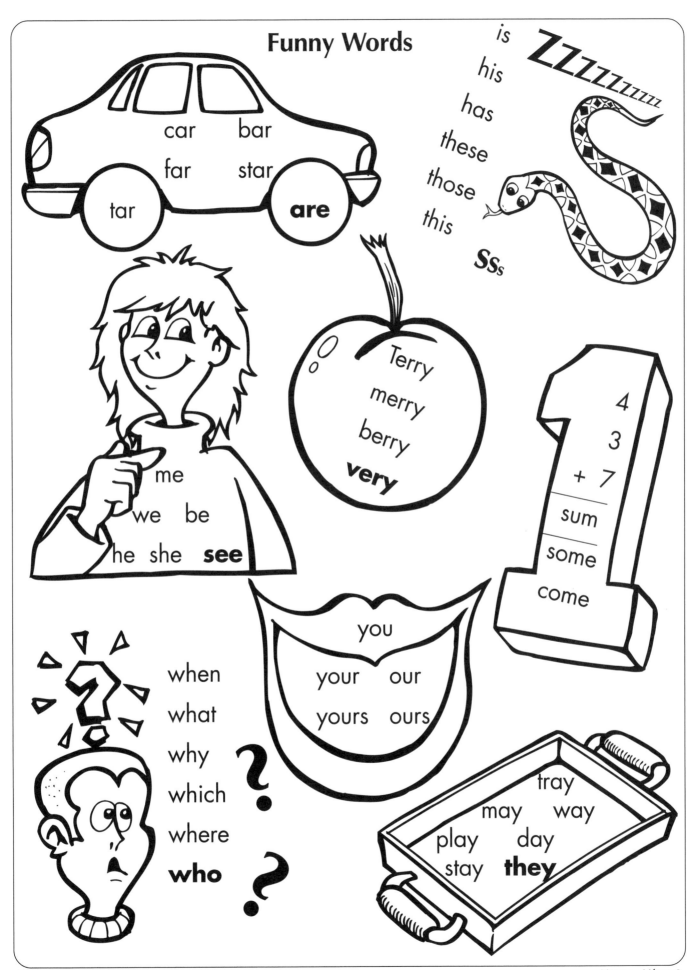

car    bar

far    star

tar    **are**

is
his
has
these
those
this
**Ss**s

ZZZZZZzzzz

Terry
merry
berry
**very**

me
we    be
he    she    **see**

4
3
+ 7
sum
some
come

when
what
why
which
where
**who**

you
your    our
yours    ours

tray
may    way
play    day
stay    **they**

© World Teachers Press® – www.worldteacherspress.com

**Trees**

Title _____

**ig**

b ___ ___

f ___ ___

p ___ ___

you

**ee**

s ___ ___

tr ___ ___

s ___ ___ d

this is

This is a fi ___ tree.

A fig tr ___ ___ has f ___ ___ s on it.

Can you s ___ ___ the figs?

**Draw a big pot of fig jam.**

☆ Figs are good for you.

They have lots of seeds in them.

© World Teachers Press® – www.worldteacherspress.com

Title _____

### ut

n _____ _____

h _____ _____

c _____ _____

### an

c _____ _____

m _____ _____

r _____ _____

make

have

N _____ _____ trees have nuts.

You c _____ _____ make a nut man.

**Draw a man in a hut.**

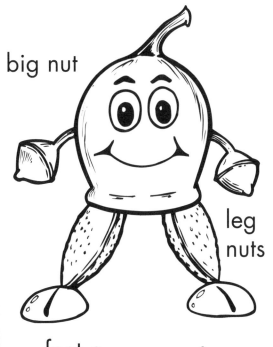

big nut

leg nuts

feet n _____ _____ s

 Some nuts are big, like coconuts.

Some are small, like peanuts.

© World Teachers Press® – www.worldteacherspress.com

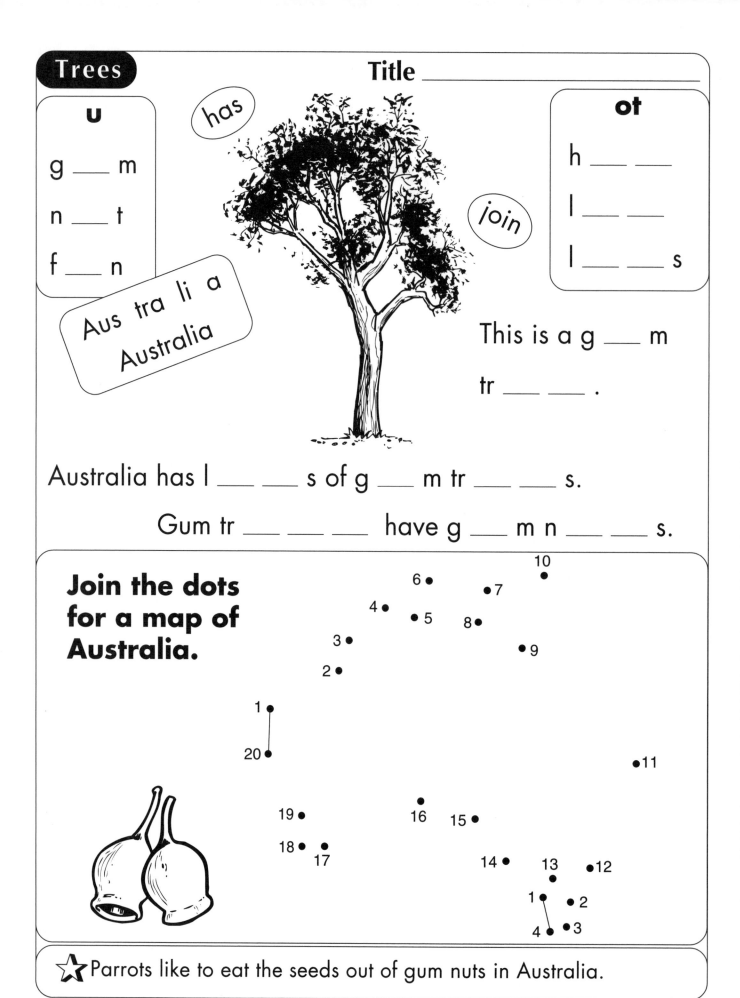

**Trees**

Title _____

**u**

g __ m

n __ t

f __ n

has

join

Aus  tra  li  a
Australia

**ot**

h __ __ __

l __ __ __

l __ __ s

This is a g __ m

tr __ __ .

Australia has l __ __ s of g __ m tr __ __ s.

Gum tr __ __ __ have g __ m n __ __ s.

**Join the dots for a map of Australia.**

6
10
4
7
5
8
3
9
2
1
20
11
19
16
15
18
17
14
13
12
1
2
4
3

⭐ Parrots like to eat the seeds out of gum nuts in Australia.

© World Teachers Press® – www.worldteacherspress.com

Title _____

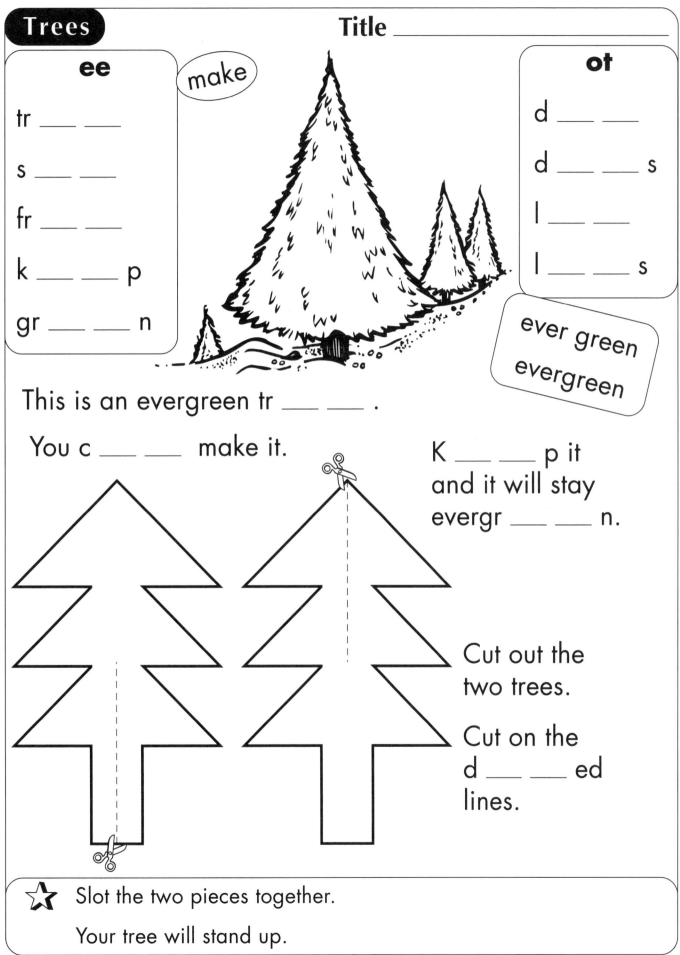

**ee**

make

tr ___ ___

s ___ ___

fr ___ ___

k ___ ___ p

gr ___ ___ n

**ot**

d ___ ___

d ___ ___ s

l ___ ___

l ___ ___ s

ever green

evergreen

This is an evergreen tr ___ ___ .

You c ___ ___ make it.

K ___ ___ p it and it will stay evergr ___ ___ n.

Cut out the two trees.

Cut on the d ___ ___ ed lines.

☆ Slot the two pieces together.

Your tree will stand up.

**Title** _____

**bu**

___ ___ g

___ ___ d

___ ___ t

 eat

leaf

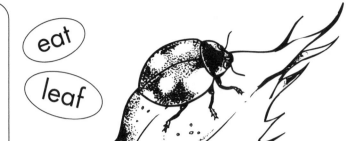

they

**eg**

l ___ ___

l ___ ___ s

p ___ ___

p ___ ___ s

This is a b ___ ___ .

Bugs have six l ___ ___ s.

This bug sits on a b ___ d.

It e ___ ___ s the bud.

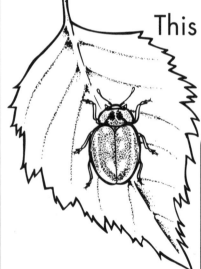

**Draw a red bug on a green leaf.**

Ladybugs are good for the garden.

They eat bugs that eat the plants.

© World Teachers Press® – www.worldteacherspress.com

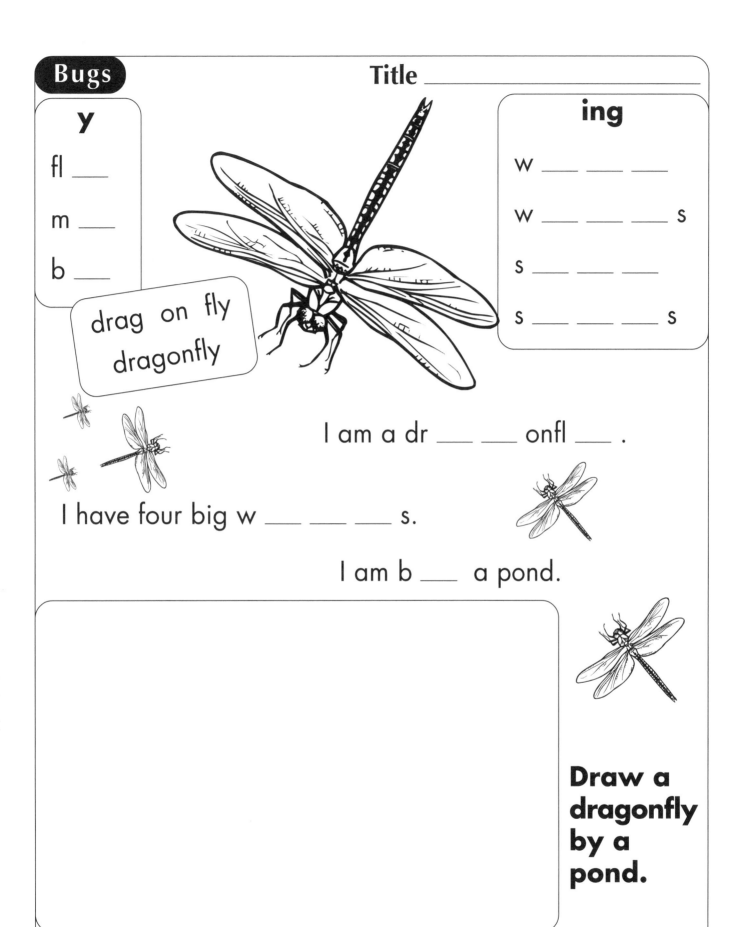

**y**

fl ___

m ___

b ___

**ing**

w ___ ___ ___

w ___ ___ ___ s

s ___ ___ ___

s ___ ___ ___ s

drag  on  fly
dragonfly

I am a dr ___ ___ onfl ___ .

I have four big w ___ ___ ___ s.

I am b ___ a pond.

**Draw a dragonfly by a pond.**

⭐ Dragonflies have very long wings that you can see through.

Title _____

**ar**

f __ __

c __ __

st __ __

very

**ong**

l __ __ __

s __ __ __

str __ __ __ __

This bug has very l __ __ __ legs.

It can hop f __ __ .

It has two w __ __ __ s.

**Draw a red and green bug with long legs.**

☆ Grasshoppers and crickets rub their legs on their wing-cases to

make a funny clicking "song."

© World Teachers Press® – www.worldteacherspress.com

**Bugs**

**Title** _____

**ang**

h ___ ___ ___

b ___ ___ ___

r ___ ___ ___

their

**y**

b ___

fl ___

m ___

Bats are animals that h ___ ___ ___ by their f ___ ___ t.

an i mals

Lots of b ___ ___ s eat bugs as they fl ___ .

**Draw a bat with a bug to eat.**

 Some bats eat fruit.

They are bigger than bats which eat bugs.

**Title** _____

**u**

p ___ p

c ___ p

t ___ b

r ___ b

called

**th**

wi ___ ___

ba ___ ___

Be ___ ___

mo ___ ___

tow  el
towel

I have a p ___ p.

She is call ___ ___ Beth.

This is Be ___ ___ in the ba ___ ___ tub.

I can r ___ b her wi ___ ___ a tow ___ ___ .

**Draw Beth with a cup of milk.**

☆ Puppies don't like to take a bath but they like to swim.

That is funny.

© World Teachers Press® – www.worldteacherspress.com

**Title** _____

**et**

v __ __

p __ __

m __ __

l __ __

said

**oo**

t __ __ k

l __ __ k

f __ __ t

b __ __ k

Jim and Sam are

my p __ __ s.

I t __ __ k Jim to the v __ __ .

"Let me l __ __ k at Jim," s __ __ d the vet.

He has a pin in his f __ __ t.

**Draw the pin in Jim's foot.**

⭐A turtle makes a good pet.

It can live in a box or in the garden.

© World Teachers Press® – www.worldteacherspress.com

**Title** _____

**ox**

f ___ ___

b ___ ___

what

**o**

g ___

n ___

s ___

This is a

big ox and

a f ___ ___ cub.

next

away

"G ___ away," said the o ___ .

"N ___ !" said the fox c ___ b.

**Draw
what
happened
next.**

 Foxes are members of the dog family.

The father is called a dog fox.

© World Teachers Press® – www.worldteacherspress.com

**cr**

___ ___ ab

___ ___ oss

___ ___ ack

her mit

hermit

**Title** _____

**ll**

wi ___ ___

she ___ ___

Bi ___ ___

live

This is my pet crab, Bi ___ ___ .

Bill is a her ___ ___ ___ cra ___ .

Bill has a big she ___ ___ to liv ___ in.

**Draw a crab shell with a crack in it.**

☆ When a hermit crab grows too big for its shell, it just finds a bigger empty one.

© World Teachers Press® – www.worldteacherspress.com

## Collecting

**ck**

lucky

ro ___ ___

so ___ ___

pi ___ ___

lu ___ ___

**x**

bo ___

mi ___

si ___

I keep them in a bo ___ .

I have lots of ro ___ ___ s.

S ___ ___ rocks fit into my bo ___ .

I am luck ___ to have my ro ___ ___ s.

**Draw me with a sack of rocks.**

 Rocks are fun to collect. There are so many different kinds.

If you break some rocks, they have pretty colors inside.

© World Teachers Press® – www.worldteacherspress.com

## Collecting

Title _____

**ar**

c ___ ___

c ___ ___ d

h ___ ___ d

some

coll ect
collect

all

b ___ ___ ___

c ___ ___ ___

sm ___ ___ ___

I coll ___ ___ ___ cards.

Some c ___ ___ ds have

ca ___ s on them.

Some have basketba ___ ___ players.

**Draw me with my stack of cards.**

⭐ Some cards of basketball or football players cost a lot of money.

**Title** _____

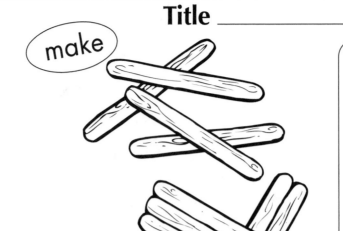

make

## st

___ ___ ick

___ ___ ack

___ ___ ep

___ ___ iff

## st

mu ___ ___

co ___ ___

be ___ ___

re ___ ___

I collect popsicle st ___ ___ ___s.

I can stick them together to m ___ ke a car, or a van or, a box.  The re ___ ___ can make a hut.

GLUE

**Draw me with my popsicle sticks.**

 If you haven't collected many popsicle sticks, you can buy them in packets.  They don't cost much.

© World Teachers Press® – www.worldteacherspress.com

Title _____

**mp**

sta ___ ___

ju ___ ___

la ___ ___

lu ___ ___

some

come

**oo**

b ___ ___ k

l ___ ___ k

f ___ ___ t

Can a da
Canada

I coll ___ ___ ___ stamps.

Some of my sta ___ ___ s come

from Can ___ ___ ___ .

I keep m ___ stamps in a big b ___ ___ k.

**Draw me with my big book of stamps.**

 Very old stamps cost a lot of money.

They are valuable.

## Coming Down

**ff**

cli ___ ___

o ___ ___

pu ___ ___

cu ___ ___

steep

cliff

**sh**

wi ___ ___

ru ___ ___

ca ___ ___

di ___ ___

rope

"Hang on.  I'm coming!"

This is a steep cli ___ ___ .

I wi ___ ___ I was on that

rope, going down that

cli ___ ___ .

**Draw the dog coming down on the rope.**

 People climb up and down cliffs.  They use strong ropes.

Their boots have rubber soles to help them grip the rocks.

© World Teachers Press® – www.worldteacherspress.com

## Coming Down

**mp**

ju _ _

lu _ _

ca _ _

bu _ _

ski

**old**

c _ _ _

b _ _ _

h _ _ _

t _ _ _

I will go for a

ski ju _ _ .

It is very c _ _ _ and I am b _ _ _ .

I hope I can ju _ _ and not fall with a big bu _ _ .

**Draw a fall and a big lump.**

☆ In some cold countries where there is lots of snow, people go ski jumping.

## Coming Down

Title _____

**ai**

( day )

r __ __ n

h __ __ l

p __ __ l

**wh**

__ __ at

__ __ ere

__ __ ich

__ __ y

What a lot

of r __ __ n.

What a

wet d __ __ .

Why is it r __ __ ning?

__ __ ere can I get dry?

__ __ en will it stop?

**Draw some hail and rain coming down on you.**

 Hailstones are frozen raindrops.

They hurt when they hit you.

© World Teachers Press® – www.worldteacherspress.com

## Coming Down

Title _____

**ay**

d ___ ___

w ___ ___

s ___ ___

st ___ ___

par a chute

parachute

**wh**

___ ___ at

___ ___ ere

___ ___ en

___ ___ y

W ___ at a

long w ___ ___

down.

Wh ___ ___ ___

am I?

Wh ___ ___ will I

feel the bu ___ ___ ?

Why am I doing this?

**Draw the parachute and you on the ground.**

Parachutes can be used for fun.  They are used for parasailing,

sky-diving, and jumping out of planes.

# Going Up

## ing

go

go ___ ___ ___

fly

fly ___ ___ ___

fast

## cket

ro ___ ___ ___ ___

po ___ ___ ___ ___

ti ___ ___ ___ ___

pa ___ ___ ___ ___

This

ro ___ ___ ___ ___

is fly ___ ___ ___

up into the sk ___ .

It is go ___ ___ ___ fast.

Can you go up in a ro ___ ___ ___ ___ ?

**Draw a ticket in your pocket for the rocket.**

⭐Soon we may be able to buy a ticket to go to the moon.

© World Teachers Press® – www.worldteacherspress.com

**Title** _____

wheel

## nd

la __ __

ha __ __

sa __ __

sta __ __

This is a jet fly __ __ __ up

in the sk __ .

It has wheels

for land __ __ __ .

## nd + ing

land __ __ __

sa __ __ __ __

sta __ __ __ __ __

It can st __ __ __ on its wh __ __ ls.

**Draw a jet landing.**

⭐ Jet planes fly all around the world.

You can fly from London to Australia in eighteen hours.

## Going Up

Title _____

**y**

sk ___

m ___

fl ___

balloons

**ing**

go ___ ___ ___

fly ___ ___ ___

do ___ ___ ___

The ball ___ ___ ___ ___ are go ___ ___ ___ up in

the sk ___ .

Soon the ___ will be

fly ___ ___ ___ far away.

they

**Draw balloons in the sky.**

 There are big hot air balloons.

People can ride in a basket under the balloon.

© World Teachers Press® – www.worldteacherspress.com

**Title** _____

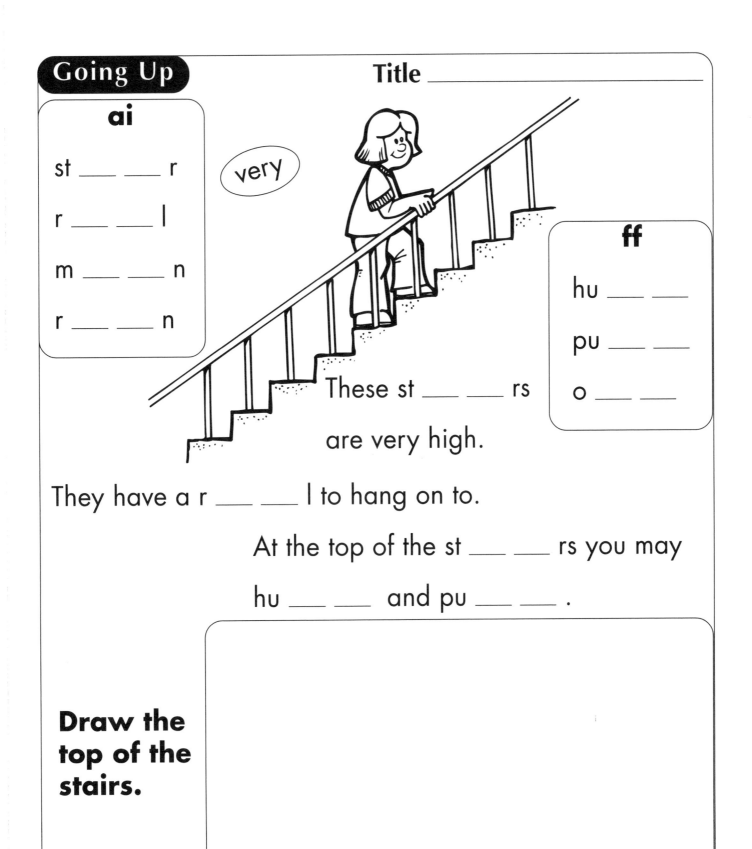

**ai**

st __ __ r

r __ __ l

m __ __ n

r __ __ n

very

**ff**

hu __ __

pu __ __

o __ __

These st __ __ rs are very high.

They have a r __ __ l to hang on to.

At the top of the st __ __ rs you may

hu __ __ and pu __ __ .

**Draw the top of the stairs.**

☆ Moving stairs are called escalators. The hand rail also moves at the same speed as the stairs. There's no huffing and puffing on them.

© World Teachers Press® – www.worldteacherspress.com

## Magic

Title _____

**ell**

w _____ _____ _____

sp _____ _____ _____

sh _____ _____ _____

t _____ _____ _____

magic

sev en

seven

**ee**

f _____ _____ t

n _____ _____ d

sh _____ _____ p

thr _____ _____

For my mag _____ _____

spe _____ _____ I will n _____ _____ d:

- six she _____ _____ s of eggs;

- seven feet of sh _____ _____ p; and

- thr _____ _____ wings of moths.

## Draw your magic pot with . . .

1  *cat's tail* _____

3  _____

2  _____

5  _____

⭐ We often draw witches on a flying broomstick with a black cat.

© World Teachers Press® – www.worldteacherspress.com

Title _____

### y

Bill ___

sill ___

funn ___

wiz  ard

wizard

### ar

wiz ___ ___ d

liz ___ ___ d

st ___ ___ s

Bill ___ is a

si ___ ___ y

wiz ___ ___ ___ .

He has a

fun ___ ___ hat

with st ___ ___ s

and moons.

He keeps a pet liz ___ ___ ___ in his hat.

**Draw
the
wizard's
lizard.**

 You can rent a video of the *Wizard of Oz* to watch at home.

© World Teachers Press® – www.worldteacherspress.com

Title _____

### ay

d __ __

w __ __

aw __ __

tod __ __

car pet

carpet

our

### o

g __

s __

n __

n __ body

Toda __ we are flying off on our

magic car __ __ __ .

We shall g __ far awa __ ,

s __ that nobod __ will see us.

**Draw the land you went to.**

 I would like to go to China on my carpet.

Where would you like to go?

© World Teachers Press® – www.worldteacherspress.com

# Magic

## ck

pi __ __

pa __ __

tri __ __

fli __ __

( you )

"Pick up that c __ __ d and look at it,

Sam," you say.

Sam l __ __ ks at the

c __ __ __ .

You have a l __ __ k

at the three of clubs.

Sam puts his card back.

## ar

c __ __ d

h __ __ d

sm __ __ t

How can you tell
Sam's card?

**Draw the
card you
think
Sam
picked.**

 Just flick through the deck until you come to the three of clubs.

Sam's card is next to it.  You are very smart!

## Cats

luck

___ ___ ___ ___ y

fluff

___ ___ ___ ___ y

mess

___ ___ ___ ___ y

Bobby

Jenny

kit  ten
kitten

Bobby and Jenny are luck ___ .

They have a little gray kit ___ ___ ___ .

She feels soft and flu ___ ___ ___ .

they
gray

**Draw her when she is messy.**

⭐ There are many different breeds of cat, from browns to blacks, short hair to long hair.  Some are fluffy and some are smooth.

© World Teachers Press® – www.worldteacherspress.com

Title _____

**st**

pa __ __

la __ __

fa __ __

cheetah

Cheet __ __ s are big cats.

They can run

very f __ __ __ .

fast

f __ __ __ er

f __ __ __ est

Ch __ __ tahs are the f __ __ __ est animal.

**Draw a
family of
cheetahs.**

☆Cheetahs live on the grasslands of Africa along with lions and

leopards.  Mother cheetahs usually have two cubs to feed.

tiger

**Title** _____

**e**

h ___

w ___

b ___

m ___

sh ___

**oo**

s ___ ___ n

m ___ ___ n

f ___ ___ d

r ___ ___ m

hab  i  tat
habitat

Tig ___ ___ s live in India.

When w ___ cut down tr ___ ___ s we cut

down tiger hab ___ ___ at.

Soon there will not b ___ much t ___ g ___ ___

ha ___ ___ ___ at left. No r ___ ___ m for the tigers.

**Draw a good tiger habitat.**

 Habitats all over the world are getting smaller.  We clear forests for farms and drain marshes for houses.  Poor animals.

© World Teachers Press® – www.worldteacherspress.com

**Title** _____

**ch**

circus

su __ __

mu __ __

ea __ __

ri __ __

**dr  tr**

d __ um

__ __ op

t __ ick

__ __ ap

At the cir __ __ __ we can see lions.

Ea __ __ lion has a d __ um to sit on.

They all do su __ __ a lot of __ __ icks.

**Draw a lion jumping in the hoop.**

 Many people don't like to see animals such as lions, elephants, or dolphins being made to do tricks.

Title _____

### bl

___ ___ ack

___ ___ ue

___ ___ ock

### mp

bu ___ ___

lu ___ ___

stu ___ ___

gru ___ ___

Bill fe ___ ___ .

He fell off a tr ___ ___  stu ___ ___ .

Bi ___ ___ fell with a big bu ___ ___ .

He wi ___ ___  have a  ___ ___ ack

and  ___ ___ ue lump.

**Draw Bill's black and blue lump.**

 A black and blue lump is called a bruise.  As the bruise goes away it turns many different colors.

© World Teachers Press® – www.worldteacherspress.com

## Colors

Title _____

**gr**

___ ___ een

___ ___ ey

___ ___ ip

par  rot

parrot

**ell**

t ___ ___ ___

y ___ ___ ___

y ___ ___ ___ ow

Some

par ___ ___ ___ s are

gr ___ ___ n and

yel ___ ___ ___ .

Some are red

and g ___ ey.

Some small parrots are b ___ ue and y ___ ___ ___ ow.

**Draw and color a parrot.**

 Parakeets are small parrots.

They are all different colors and people keep them as pets.

Title _____

**ll**

gives

i __ __

pi __ __ s

Wi __ __ y

si __ __ y

Wi __ __ y is sick.

Wh __ n Willy is i __ __ , he looks

wh __ t __ , and he has to stay in be __ .

His doctor giv __ __ him pi __ __ s.

**wh**

__ __ en

__ __ ich

__ __ ite

**Draw Willy feeling better.**

 When we are sick our temperature often goes up.  We have to stay in bed until our temperature is back to normal.

© World Teachers Press® – www.worldteacherspress.com